Take That Books is an imprint of
Take That Ltd.
P.O.Box 200
Harrogate
HG1 4XB

Written and illustrated by Russell Jones

Australian Associate:
MaxiBooks, P.O.Box 529, Kiama, NSW 2533, Australia.

10 9 8 7 6 5 4 3 2 1

ISBN 1-873668-65-1

Layout and typesetting by
Impact Design, P.O.Box 200, Harrogate, HG1 4XB.

Printed and bound in Great Britain.

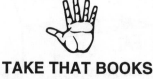

TAKE THAT BOOKS

THAT'S HER FIFTH MULTIPLE ORGASM THIS WEEK!
MIAOW!! MIAOW!!
MIAOW!! MIAOW!!
MIAOW!!
MIAOW!!
MIAOW!! MIAOW!!
MIAOW!!

BEHOLD! TWO DOGS IN A BACK ALLEY. CRUDE... PRIMITIVE... FEEBLE MINDED.... A SORT OF CANINE JURASSIC PARK!

MIHOW!
MIAOW! MIAOW!
MIAOW! MIAOW! MIAOW!
MIIAOW! MIAOW! MIAOW! MIAOW!
MIAOW! MIAOW! MIAOW! MIAOW!
MIAOW! MIAOW! MIAOW! MIAOWAAAAAAH!
MIAOW! MIAOW! MIAOWAAAAAAAAAAH!
MIAOWAAAAAAAAAAAAAHH
SHE FAKES ORGASM BETTER THAN MEG RYAN!

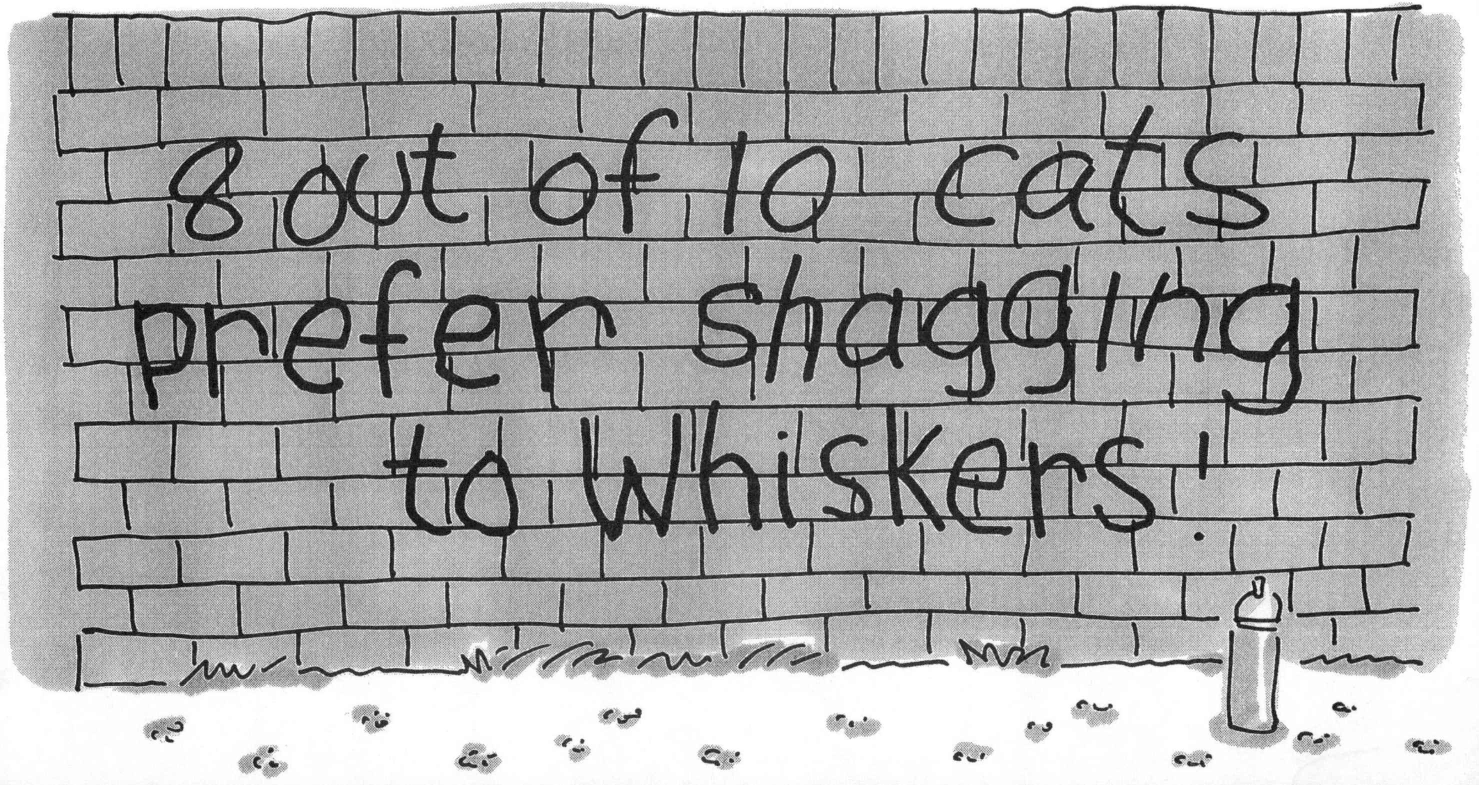
8 out of 10 cats
prefer shagging
to Whiskers!

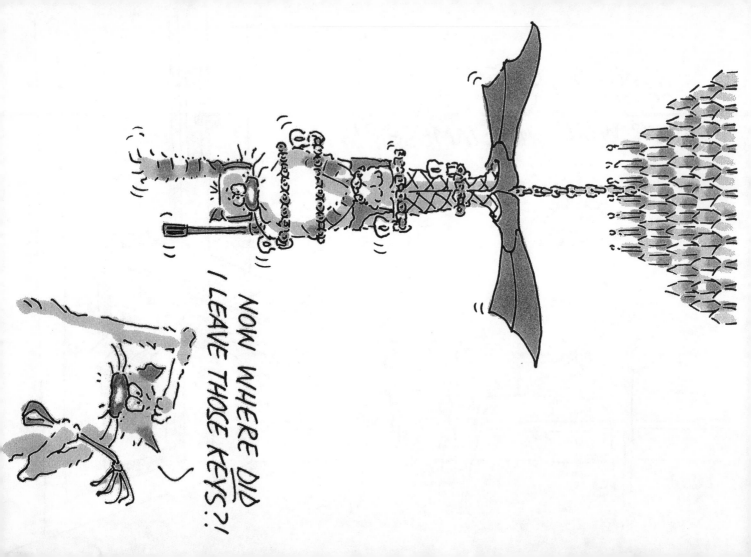

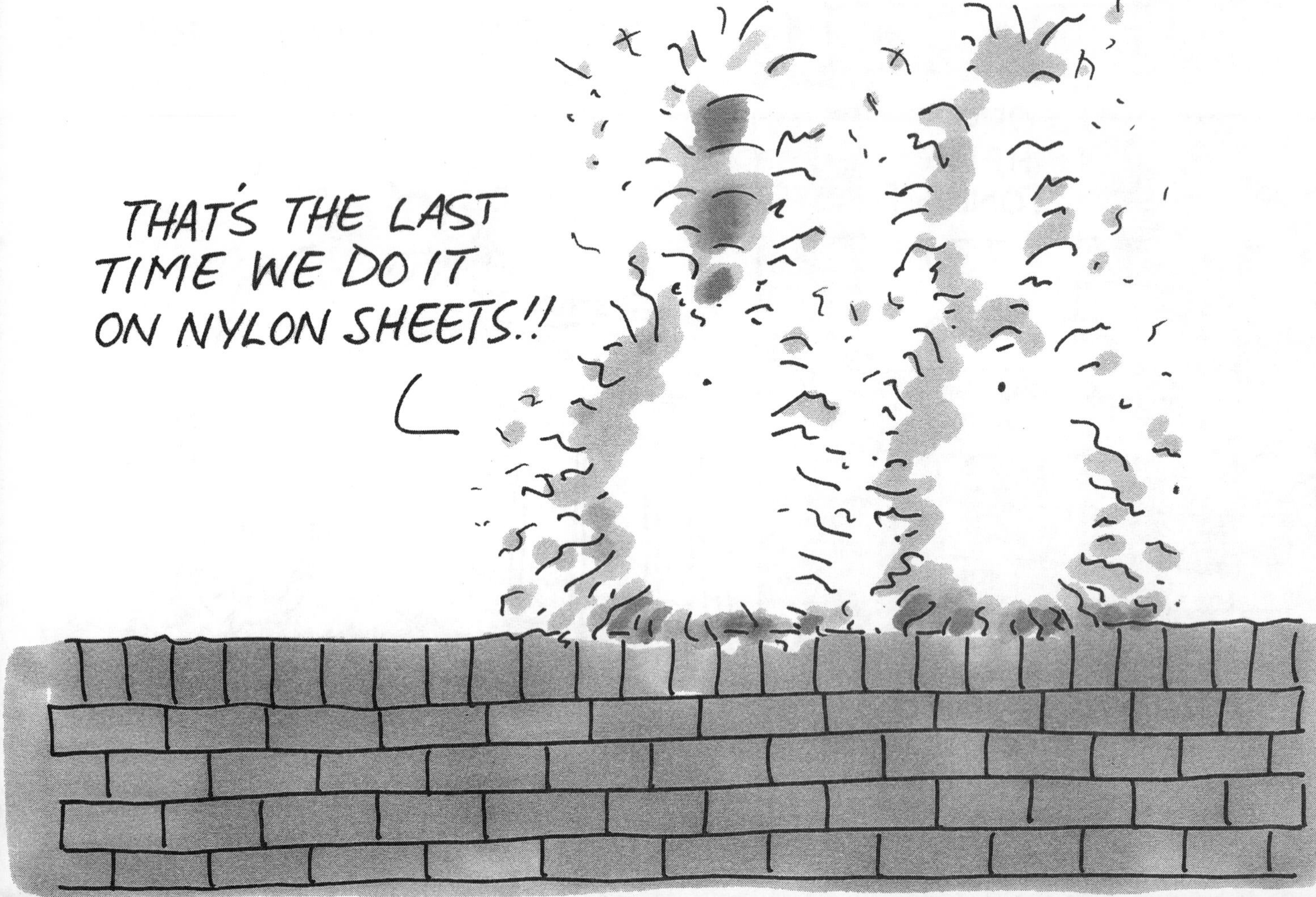
THAT'S THE LAST TIME WE DO IT ON NYLON SHEETS!!

I ALWAYS KNEW AN ORGY ON A FOLD-UP BED WAS A BAD IDEA!

FOUND IT IN THE BUSHES. GOT NO IDEA WHAT IT IS BUT IT CERTAINLY KEEPS THE RAIN OUT!

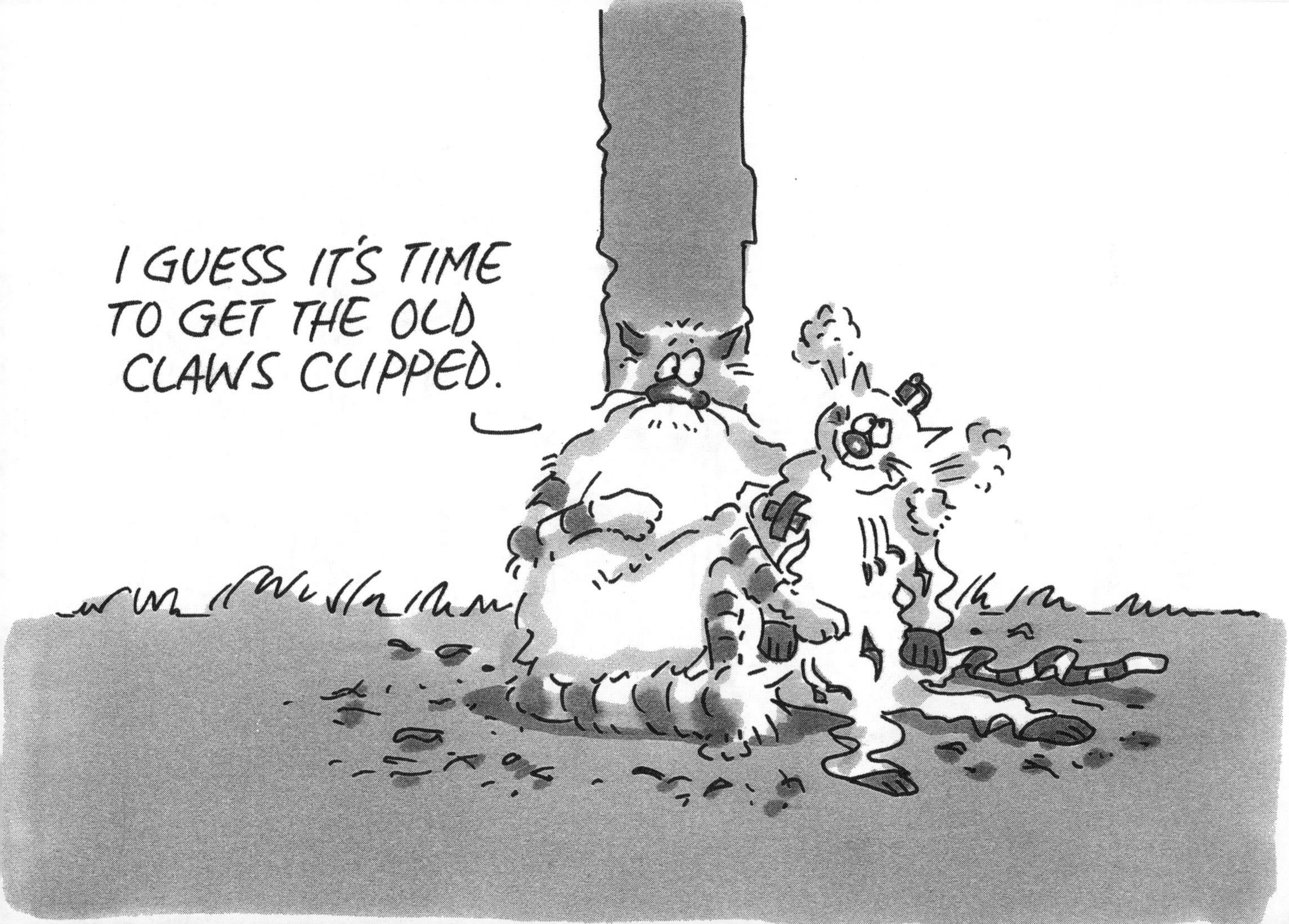
I GUESS IT'S TIME TO GET THE OLD CLAWS CLIPPED.

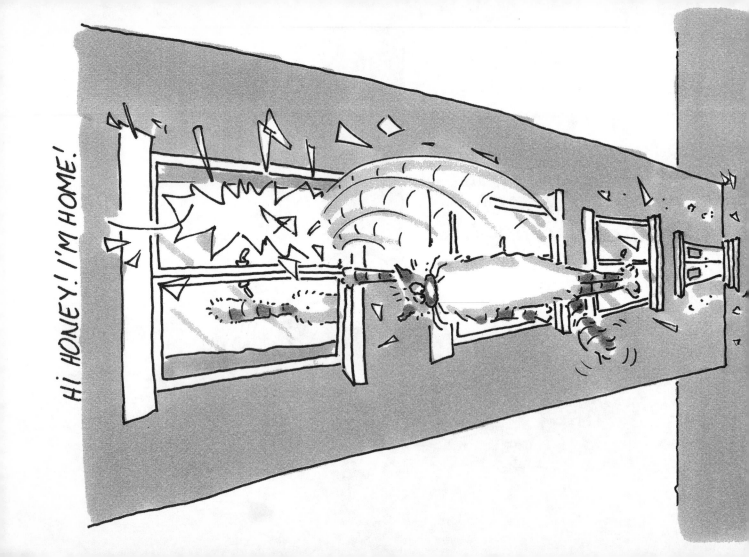

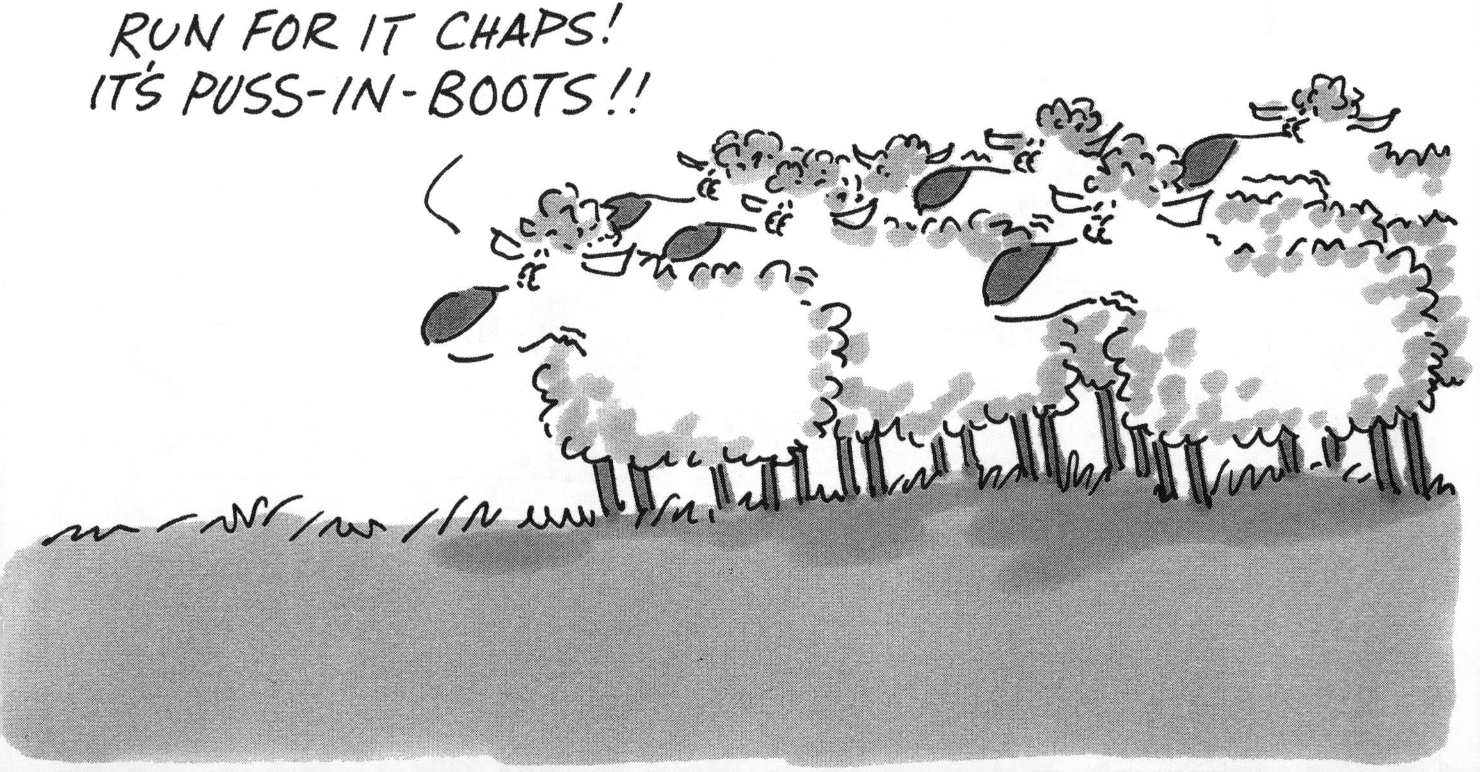
RUN FOR IT CHAPS!
IT'S PUSS-IN-BOOTS!!

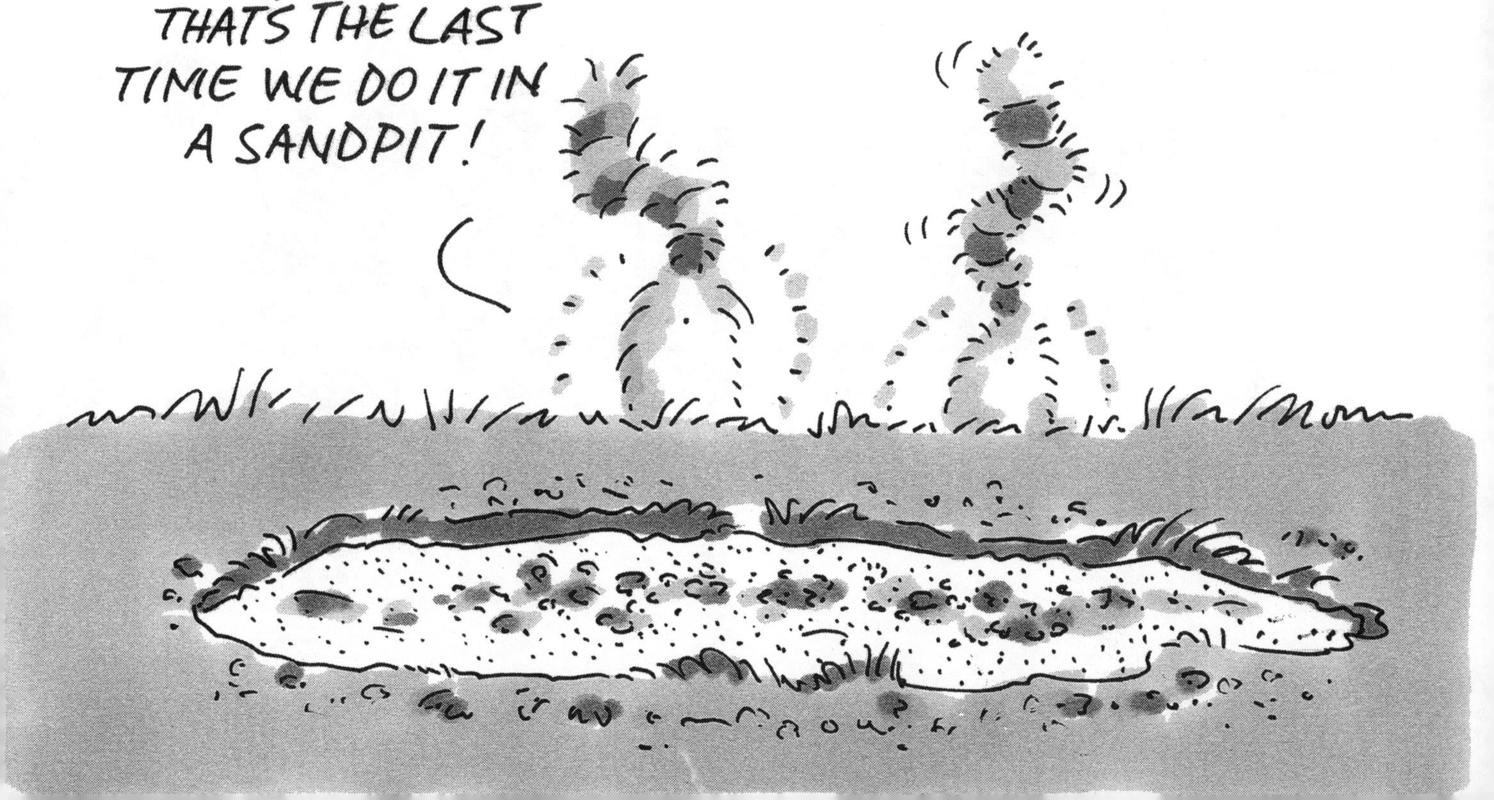
THAT'S THE LAST TIME WE DO IT IN A SANDPIT!

MORE HUMOUR TITLES...

The Ancient Art of Farting *by Dr. C.Huff*
Ever since time began, man (not woman) has farted. Does this ability lie behind many of the so far unexplained mysteries of history? You Bet - because Dr. C.Huff's research shows conclusively there's something rotten about history taught in schools. If you do most of your reading on the throne, then this book is your ideal companion. Sit back and fart yourself silly as you split your sides laughing! *£3.99*

A Wunch of Bankers
Do you HATE BANKS? Then you need this collection of stories aimed directly at the crotch of your bank manager. A Wunch of Bankers mixes cartoons and jokes about banks with real-life horror stories of the bare-faced money-grabbing tactics of banks. If you think you've been treated badly, read these stories!!!! *£3.99*

The Hangover Handbook & Boozer's Bible
(In the shape of a beercan)
Ever groaned, burped and cursed the morning after, as Vesuvius erupted in your stomach, a bass drummer thumped on your brain and a canary fouled its nest in your throat? Then you need these 100+ hangover remedies. There's an exclusive Hangover Ratings Chart, a Boozer's Calendar, a Hangover Clinic, and you can meet the Great Drunks of History, try the Boozer's Reading Chart, etc., etc. *£3.99*

Down the Pan: Amuse Yourself in the Toilet
Do you have fun in the toilet? Or, do you merely go about your business and then depart? Instead of staring at the floor and contemplating the Universe, you could be having a ball. Here is an hilarious collection of *cartoons, jokes* and *silly stories*... a gruesome description of *great toilet accidents*... Discover the *secret card tricks* which are certain to impress your friends... Europeans may turn straight to the *Franglais conversation* sur la bog... Look at *famous toilets of history*... Learn how to *juggle toilet rolls*! *£3.99*

A Slow Screw Against the wall (& Other Cocktails)
Over 200 recipes for luscious and lively cocktails. Even the most serious of cocktail drinkers will find something new for their taste buds to savour. £3.99

The Beerlover's Bible & Homebar Handbook
(also in the shape of a beercan)
Do you love beer? Then this is the book you've been waiting for - a tantalising brew of fascinating facts to help you enjoy your favourite fluid all the more. Discover how to serve beer for maximum enjoyment... brew your own... entertain with beer... cook tasty recipes... and more! Includes an exhaustive listing of beers from all over the world with their flavours, colours and potency. You'll become a walking encyclopedia on beer! £3.99

MORE GOOD BOOKS...

The National Lottery Book: Winning Strategies

An indispensable guide to the hottest lottery systems in the world. All designed to help you find those lucky lottery numbers that could make you rich. ● Learn how to *Play Like the Pros*... ● Discover ways of *Getting an Edge*... ● Improve your chances with the '*Wheeling Technique*'... ● Find possible ways of *Making it Happen* for you... ● See how understanding betting *Psychology and Equitability* can seriously *Improve Your Winnings*... ● Plus lots more *General Tips* to help you win! £4.99

For a free full colour catalogue of all titles, please send an SAE to the address below.

A Load of Bollards (for motorists everywhere)

Road cones are about to achieve their galactic mission - to take control of all major road networks. Breeding like rabbits. Moving only at night. Causing chaos as they appear from nowhere. Will the motorists nightmare never end?... £3.99

The Armchair Guide to Football

An inexpensive and humorous look at the state of modern football. Is it really run by money crazed businessmen who don't care about tradition? Just what are journalists on when they write their reports? And, will Fantasy Football remove the need for pitches, players and footballs? Only £1.99

The Armchair Guide to Fishing

Just why do people go fishing? Is it the basic hunting instinct or do we just love drowning maggots? More to the point, who in their right mind really wants to go to work, or stay at home with the kids, when there are fish out there to be caught? No wonder fishing is the UK's most popular outdoor participant sport. Only £1.99

The Armchair Guide to Golf

An invaluable addition to the library of anyone irrevocably addicted to the game. From the serious handicap hunter to the weekend hacker, everybody will appreciate this humorous view from the 'inside'. Even those who have thrown in the towel on their golfing careers will be able to laugh, alongside all those golfing widows and widowers. Only £1.99